JAMAICAN WORD DICTIONARY
and
Short Stories About Language

JAMAICAN WORD DICTIONARY
and
Short Stories About Language

Deeta S. Johnson

ARTHUR H. STOCKWELL LTD
Torrs Park, Ilfracombe, Devon, EX34 8BA
Established 1898
www.ahstockwell.co.uk

*British Library Cataloguing-in-Publication Data.
A catalogue record for this book is available
from the British Library.*

ISBN 978-0-7223-4489-7
*Printed in Great Britain by
Arthur H. Stockwell Ltd
Torrs Park   Ilfracombe
Devon EX34 8BA*

CONTENTS

HISTORY

The island of Jamaica is thought to have been uninhabited until the Arawak Indians arrived from the mainland of America, about ten centuries before the earliest Spanish settlers.

The Arawaks named the island XAYMACA, meaning 'Land of Wood and Water'.

The Arawak population declined when the Spanish settlers moved in. Negro slaves were imported from Africa to cultivate the island for the first time in the fifteen century. The capital or new township, Spanish Town, was established in what is now St Catherine in the county of Middlesex.

In the sixteenth century, the British captured the island from the Spanish. Most of the Spaniards were expelled from the island and made their way to Cuba and other places. Some fled to the hills and formed a settlement.

Jamaica was now under British rule. More slaves

were brought in to grow crops such as sugar cane, coffee, tobacco and cocoa. Some African slaves rebelled against the British and joined the settlers in the hills. The descendants of these settlers exist in these areas to this day.

The capital was moved to Kingston in 1872.

English is the official language. A dialect known as patois, spoken by the indigenous people, is presented in this book.

The majority of the population belong to Christian denominations.

The judicial system in Jamaica is based on British law.

PROFILE

Jamaica is an island in the Caribbean Sea. The closest Caribbean islands to Jamaica are Haiti to the east and Cuba to the north. Jamaica is also close to Florida, which lies north of Cuba in the Southern States of America.

Jamaica is a well-established tourist resort with beautiful white sandy beaches. The daily temperature ranges from 30 to 33 degrees Celsius all year round.

Jamaica has a rich tapestry of people and entertainment, and flora and fauna.

The island is popular with tourists worldwide, especially those from the USA, owing to its close proximity.

Jamaica has two international airports, one at either end of the island – namely, Kingston and Montego Bay.

CLIMATE

There are many rivers in Jamaica, with waterfalls and rapids. Some rivers disappear underground through limestone and reappear again as mineral springs. The mineral springs are famous as spa baths and other tourist attractions.

The hottest months in Jamaica are June to September and the rainy season is October to November.

PREFACE

Jamaican patois is extensively used in Jamaica and in Jamaican communities around the world. It is spoken with a distinct accent, and used especially when singing reggae and dance-hall songs.

Jamaica is an English-speaking country, but a large percentage of the indigenous people choose to speak the Jamaican patois.

If the Jamaican patois is spoken in a television documentary or drama, it is broad enough to warrant subtitles.

The language is comprised of words taken from other languages over the centuries and it has its origins in a time when the Jamaican economy was based on slavery.

The language comprises English, Spanish, African, Dutch, Creole and Portuguese words and has been skilfully coined and devised by the native Jamaicans.

Jamaica was first inhabited by the Arawak Indians, a migrating race of people from South America. Jamaica was later discovered by Columbus in 1494 and was named 'Jamaica' when he discovered the Americas.

After the Spanish rule the island was ruled by the British for over 300 years, and gained independence in August 1962. Jamaicans are a mixture of different nationalities since 1494 with surnames (and place names) originating from England, Scotland, Ireland, Spain, France, Africa, Portugal and Holland – in fact names encompassing all five inhabited continents of the globe.

The Jamaican patois is used in books, newspapers and advertising, and on radio programmes in Jamaica.

My first impression on overhearing the patois was that it sounded light-hearted – i.e. it is fruity, fun and airy and it rolls off the tongue easily. It can even sound romantic – romantic because it is created by the people. Whether spoken or sung, it can be used to express joy, gaiety, anger, seriousness, frivolity and simplicity. The old words have been handed down from generation to generation, and thousands of new words are being formed by present-day Jamaicans. Poets, singers, thespians and other wordsmiths find the language quite funny to play with.

It is not a recent language, but it is still evolving. So there is a growing trend to preserve the Jamaican patois.

FOOTNOTE
Double-barrelled words and phrases form a great part of the language. Therefore, it is difficult to understand and speak the language without incorporating them. And it is the nuances which make the language colourful.

ODE TO JAMAICA

There is an isle, a sunny isle,
Down the Caribbean way.
It is known as the land of wood and water –
Jamaica is the name.
Jamaica, Xaymaca, I pray ye remain,
In God's good grace to ever strive
From strength to strength in love and praise.

Valiant and brave from dawn to dusk
Their hearts and feet outshine the sun.
Time to rest, sleep and avoid the dust,
To leave the night for the crickets' cry
And the guiding light when the fireflies fly.

Ye people of this land rejoice,
Let joy and love remain.
Ye land of wood and water,
Let peace in your hearts prevail.

A – Z
JAMAICAN
WORD
DICTIONARY

A

A	Pronounced as the vowel 'a' in words before or after a consonant.
Ackee	Vegetable. Ackee and Saltfish is a native dish.
Adda	Other.
A fi we	It is ours – plural.
A goh	*Mi a goh* – I am going.
Ah it mek	That is why – The reason is.
Aise	Ear(s) – singular or plural.
A mi	It is I – me.
An	And, on.
Anansi (n.)	Spider.
Anedda	Another.
Angle	Handle.
Anh (n.)	Hand.
Appen	Occurred (past tense, 'H' not sounded).

Areddi	Already, done, finish.
Aring/Arinj (n.)	Orange.
Arti farti	Hesitant action.
At (n.)	Hat.
Auda	Order.
A wah?	What is it?
A wah dis?	What is this?
A weh?	Where is it?
Awoah	Expression of defiance: I will not.
Awrite	Greeting: All right.
Ax	Ask (a question).
Axe	A tool for chopping wood.
Aye	Greeting: Hello.
Aye sah	A sigh of impatience or disgust.

B

Backanda	Money. A bribe.
Backchat	To be disrespectful to one's elder.
Backra	White landowner. Rich landlord/farmer.
Badda	*No badda* – Don't worry, forget it.
Baddarashan	Worries, trouble, problems.
Bad-wud	Swear word. To swear at.
Baffan	Disabled person, mentally or physically.
Baggi	Small girl's knickers.
Ball head	Short hairstyle, not dreadlocks.
Bambye	To save for later (e.g. food).
Bammy/Bammie	Flat cassava cake sold in shops.
Bangarang	Noise, commotion. People arguing or fighting.

Bankra (n.)	Wicker basket for farm foods, etc.
Barbecue	An elevated outdoor patio to dry coffee, pimento, etc.
Barra	Borrow. To borrow something.
Batty	Bottom, bum, sacrum.
Bax-bout	Move frequently. Unsettled.
Beggi-beggi	Very greedy.
Bickle (n.)	Ancient word for food, cooked or not.
Big up (v.)	To praise someone or applaud something.
Black-heart man	Another name for bogeyman, told to children. A myth.
Blasted	Expressing anger (i.e. swearing).
Bokkle	Bottle.
Boofootu	Fat, obese person.
Boot	Ankle shoes or boots.
Bout	About.
Box-bout	Moving about here and there. Inconsistent.
Brawta	To give a few extra (e.g. grains, fruits, etc).
Bred	Bread. Slang for money.
Bredda	Brother, male sibling.
Bredren	Relatives. Related to each other.

Breed	Pregnant. *Breeding* is to be pregnant.
Bruckins	Dancing, incorporating freestyle moves.
Bruk	Broke. Having no money. Broken goods, etc.
Brukfuss	Breakfast.
Buck up	To meet an acquaintance. A surprise.
Bud (n.)	Bird.
Buddy	Small boy's penis (i.e. toddler).
Bula cake	Flat cheap cake sold in shops.
Bumbo	Swear word relating to bottom, bum.
Bungle (n.)	Parcel (small or large).
Busha	White landlord. Farm owner.
Bush tea	Tea made from a garden herb (e.g. mint).
Bwoy	Boy (expressed with anger).

C

Caafe	Coffee.
Caan	Corn, maize, polenta.
Caana	Corner. Round a bend.
Cacca	Part of a swear word.
Caccati	Proud, snobbish person.
Callaloo	Green-leafed vegetable like spinach.
Catty	Vagina (i.e. young girl).
Ceresse	Bitter bush for medicinal tea.
Chaka chaka	Messy, untidy place (e.g. room).
Chalklit	Cocoa beans. Chocolate drink.
Chek	Look.
Chek mi	Call me later.
Chew stick	Tree bark used to clean teeth.
Chikeney business	Dodgy dealings.
Cho-cho	Green vegetable produce.
Choosday	Tuesday.
Chowy-chowy	Poor taste, texture (e.g. fruit or vegetable).

Chuck	Throw something carelessly.
Chuku-chuku	To wash carelessly (e.g. clothes). By hand
Claat	Cloth. Part of a swear word.
Coali-coali	Shy, quiet, reserved.
Cocci	Confident. Penis.
Comougin	Secretive, cagey person.
Coodeh	Look here.
Coomu-coomu	Cagey, private person.
Cooyah	Expression of contempt.
Corroson	Noise. Commotion.
Cotch	Sit somewhere uncomfortable (i.e. temporarily).
Craben	Greedy for food.
Cutlass	Machete. large knife to chop wood and grass etc.
Cut yeye	Look at someone angrily.

D

Dan	Than.
Dark	Not clever. Lacking intelligence.
Dase	Days.
Dat	That.
Dawg	Dog. Domestic pet.
Dawta	Daughter.
De	The.
De De	Common word for faeces.
Dedeh	It is there.
Dedi-dedi	Not energetic. Not looking lively.
Deggeh	One – only one. Solo.
Deh	There.
Deh so/Dere	There.
Deh wid	Is with (i.e. a relationship, man and woman).
Deh yah?	He/she is here?

Dem	They.
Den mi nah tell yuh	This is what I am saying/mean.
Dinna	Dinner.
Draws	Old woman's knickers, large with strings.
Dreadlocks	Hairstyle worn by Rastas, male or female.
Dreddi	Nickname for man with dreadlocks.
Dress-back	A command: Move backwards. Give me some space.
Dry foot	Someone with stick-like legs.
Dry head	A woman with very short hair (i.e. balding or problem with growth).
Duck	Bend head quickly to avoid a blow.
Dun	Finish. It is done.
Dundus	Albino. Person lacking dark pigment in skin, hair or eyes.
Dung	Down.
Dung deh	Over there. Down there.
Dung yah	Down here.
Duppy	Ghost. Apparition.
Dutchie	Iron cooking pot.
Dutty	Dirty.
Dweet (v.)	Do it. To do something.

E

Eeeh	To answer or respond to one's name (i.e. yes).
Eeena	Inside (a shop, car or room).
Eena	Into. Into something (a job or queue).
Eggs up	Too pushy. Precocious.
Engka	Waiting for something, (e.g. food). Greedy.
Even up	Pushy – too friendly.
Extra	To show off. Flirty. Extrovert.
Eyrie	Greeting: Hello. All right.

F

Faas	Someone who interferes. Interfering.
Facesty	Feisty. Fiery person. Cheeky. Rude.
Fadda	Father.
Fallah	Follow.
Fambly	Family or relative.
Fassi	Damaged skin (sores, eczema, etc.). Difficult to heal. Infected.
Fava	To look like someone or resemble something.
Fenke fenke	Fussy, hard to please. Fastidious.
Fenneh	A warning: You will be sorry.
Fe we	It is ours.
Fi/fe mi	For. For me.
Field	Farm/allotment.

Fingle	To handle.
Finike	Strange or peculiar (e.g. dislike or fear of something).
Fitiging	Annoying.
Flatter	Convulsion, of person or animal.
Fling (v.)	To throw something.
Flittaz (n.)	Savoury pancake made with flour, fish and herbs.
Fluxy	Semi-ripe fruit. Not fully grown.
Foce up	Someone who is too friendly.
Fool-fool	Simpleton. Person of low intelligence.
Foot battam	Sole of the feet/foot.
Fram	From. Away from. Come from.
Fren	Friend. My friend.
Fresh	To be disrespectful to someone.
Frig-up	Description of someone who is unreliable.
Frowsy	Foul-smelling place or person.
Fyah	Fire.

G

Gad, Gawd	God. Lord.
Gal	Girl.
Gallang	Go away. Go on. Walk away.
Ganja	Cannabis, marijuana.
Ganzee	Jumper, pullover.
Gimme	Give it to me.
Ginnal	Crafty. Conman.
Girout	Get lost. Leave me alone.
Gizada (n.)	Small pastry cake filled with grated coconut and sugar.
Goh	Go. To go. Go on. Leave.
Goodeh	Went there or going there.
Gourdie	Utensil made from calabash.
Gouzoo	Another word for obeah or voodoo.
Go-weh (v)	Go away.
Gravalishus	Greedy. Materialistic.
Green tea	Tea made from garden herbs.

Grine	Shaking the hips to music or sex.
Grip	Old suitcase for travel, etc.
Grung	Farm. Field where produce is grown.
Gully	Narrow, deep space in forest.
Gwaan	Stop doing whatever.
Gwine (v.)	Going to. About to do something.

H

Hab	To have something.
Haffi (v.)	I have to do/give/go, etc.
Haggish	Aggressive or acting that way.
Hail	Greeting: Hello.
Har	Her.
Hard dough (n.)	Solid unsliced bread.
Hat	Hot.
Hath	Hurt. Painful. To feel pain.
Haus	Horse.
Havvi	I have it.
Heat (v.)	To eat.
Herb	Cannabis, marijuana.
Hightey-tightey	Someone who is prim and proper, usually a female.
Hile (n.)	Oil (cooking oil, hair oil, lubricating oil, etc.).
Hole	Get hold of something. Hold it. A hole.
Hood	Man's penis.

Hood	Wood (lumber, tree, etc.).
Housecoat	Dressing gown.

I

Igle	Idle. Lazy.
I-man	Me, myself.
Inglan	England.
Inna	Into.
Irie	Greeting: I'm all right. Are you?
Irish potato	Spuds (white only), potato.
Ischool	High school, college. Secondary/private education.
Ital	Clean, fresh, natural foods.

J

JA	Jamaica.
Jackass	Male donkey.
Jacket	To falsely accuse a man of fathering a child.
Jah	Rastafarian name for God.
Jam	Stuck (e.g. door). Crowd of dancers.
Jamdung	Name for Jamaica (1970s).
Jancrow (n.)	Vulture. Blackbird. Crow.
Jancrow batty	Overproof white rum (100%).
Jeezam	Expression of amazement or surprise.
Jilapy (n.)	Old motor vehicle, car, etc.
Jing bang	People behaving badly. Crowd.
Jizzle	Light rain.
Jonkonnu	Masquerade with drums, music, etc.

Jonny cake (n.)	Fried dumpling.
Jook	To prick someone or something.
Junjo	Fungus. Wild mushroom.

K

Kanana pooh	To say nothing. Keep silent. No comment.
Kananga water	Locally made eau de cologne.
Kattah (n.)	Cushion. Padding on head to support load.
Kawn	Callus. Hard skin on foot.
Kawz	Cause.
Kersine (n.)	Paraffin oil for lamp or stove.
Khus khus (n.)	Perfume made from local plants.
Kibba (v.)	To cover (e.g. a pot).
Kinoba	To faint suddenly.
Kip	Keep. Keep it.
Kiss Teet	A hissing sound made by drawing air in through the teeth when annoyed or disgusted (a common occurrence).

Kohle kohle	Quiet, uninteresting person (e.g. shy).
Kole	Cold. Low temperature.
Kotch (v.)	To share a room temporarily.
Kriss	Something in a clean, new, tidy condition.
Kulu-kulu (n.)	Unrefined. Overproof white rum.
Kweez	Squeeze, tight fit (e.g. shoes).

L

Laas	Lost. To lose something.
Labrish	News. Gossip between friends.
Lamps	To con someone. To fool.
Lawd	Lord. God.
Leff	Leave or left/gone.
Likki likki	Someone who likes something free.
Likkle	Small, little (e.g. amount).
Lilli	Small (person or thing).

M

Maaga	Underweight. Skinny person.
Macka	Thorn from prickly plant.
Mah/Ma	Mam (i.e. woman).
Mah-mah man	An effeminate male.
Malarki	Skylarking. Not serious.
Mampie (n.)	Extra-large girlfriend or wife.
Mash mash (n.)	Extra portion of something.
Maskitta	Mosquito.
Massa	Sir (i.e. mister).
Massi	Mercy. *Lawd a massi*.
Maw (n.)	Cow's stomach, intestines.
Mawnin	Morning.
Mek (v.)	To make/do something.
Mek-mek	Coy. Undecided.
Memba	Remember. Church member.
Merino	Vest, underwear.
Mi	Me. I.
Mi ah	I am.

Mi nah	I am not.
Moutha massi	Loud mouth (i.e. female).
Mumma	Mother. Curse word.

N

Nagah	Negro.
Nah	Not.
Nahsi (adj.)	Nasty.
Natty	Short name for a natty dread.
Natty dread	Rastafarian.
Nebah	Never.
Neegle	Needle.
Nenyam (n.)	Uncooked food (possibly African).
Nex	Next. Who is next?
Nigger	Negro.
Nize	Noise.
No	No.
Nuff	Plenty.
Nuh	I do not. Don't know.
Nyam (v.)	To eat (possibly African).

O

Obeah	A type of witchcraft. To practise witchcraft.
Ol' bruck	An old person who is poor.
Ole anh	Hold it. Wait. Stop, halt.
Ol' yard	A past residence.
Onda	Under, below.
Ongle	Only. One.
Ooman	Woman.
Ooo?	Who? A query (i.e. question mark).
Ouse	House. Abode.
Ouse top	Roof or top of house.
Outa	Out of (part of a sentence). Out of doors. Outside.

P

Pakki	Small bowl made from calabash tree.
Pap	Porridge for baby (e.g. green banana and cornmeal i.e. polenta).
Pappishow	To show off. To disgrace oneself.
Partner	A kind of club in which a trustworthy person collects a sum of money each week and gives it all back to a different individual each week.
Patooh-patoo	An owl. The sound of the bird.
Pattie	Pasty (curry, meat or vegetable).
Patty	Curry goat patty. Takeaway snack shaped like a pasty.
Pear	Avocado (called 'pear' because of the shape).

Peel-head	Bald-headed man.
Peeling skin	Vegetable peel (i.e. potato, carrot, yam, banana, etc.).
Peenie wallie	Firefly displaying a faint flashing light. Insect.
Pee pee	To pass urine.
Pepperpot	Spicy soup or stew.
Pickey	Fussy. Particular.
Pickey pickey	Fussy about everything.
Pickney	Small girl or boy.
Pissabout (adj.)	Someone fooling around (e.g. ramp).
Plantin	Plantain. A food similiar to banana that is eaten boiled, fried or roasted.
Poco-mania	A religious sect of people who dance and go into trances (Spanish word).
Poco poco	So and so. Mixed feelings.
Pocoterie	In trouble, worries.
Pon	Upon.
Pone	Pudding made with sweet potato or cornmeal.
Pooh pooh	To open the bowels. Faeces.
Poom pan	Kitchen utensil. Bowl made from tin.
Poom poom	Young female's vagina.

Porkie	Vagina (i.e. young girl's).
Posse	Friends. Gang.
Prekkeh	Someone acting silly. Immature adult.
Puddung	Put down (something).
Pum-pum	Another spelling for young girl's vagina.
Punnani	Vagina (i.e. woman's).
Punni	Vagina (i.e. young girl's).
Puppa	Father. Papa.
Puppa-lick	Somersault. To tumble, roll over repeatedly.
Puss boots	Cheap shoes made from cloth or crêpe.
Pussy	Vagina (i.e. woman's).
Puth puth	Mud. Soft clay.
Puttus	Romantic name for woman.
Putto putto	Wet, muddy area.
Pyah pyah	Weak-minded (man). Not spirited.

Q

Quabs	Not friends with (i.e. in a different class).
Quashi	Anyone acting silly.
Quattie	Old coin of low value.
Quinge up	To hug oneself (e.g. on feeling the cold).

R

Raas	A swear word relating to a part of the body, used on its own or joined to another swear word.
Raatid	Mild swear word expressing surprise.
Ramp	To play (e.g. children playing).
Rasta	Someone who is a Rastafarian.
Rastafarian	Relating to a religion or cultural way of life founded in Jamaica.
Rawchaw	Uncouth, ignorant person.
Red yeye	Greedy. Jealous.
Reggae	Dance hall music composed in Jamaica by various artists, including Bob Marley.
Renk	Cheeky, feisty, presumptuous.
Res	Rest. Relax. Stop for a while.

Righted	Sane. Sensible. Used after 'not' to describe someone acting insane.
Rite	Right.
Roux	To have sex with (male to female).
Rox	To be cross with someone verbally.
Ruffian	An old yob.
Rundung	Native dish of mackerel cooked in coconut milk.
Runmouth	Slanderer.

S

Sah	Sir (in conversation).
Salimonie	To worry, fret or moan constantly.
Salting	Fish or meat for dinner.
Sankey	Hymn book.
Sap	To bathe a painful part of the body.
Scobeech	To season fried fish with vinegar, onions, pepper and salt.
Seet deh	Look at this. There it is.
Sheg	Another word for having sex.
Shegging	Swear word expressing annoyance.
Sheg up	Phrase describing someone unreliable.
Shingle	Lathe used for roofing.
Shut	Shirt.

Shuth	Shut (door, window, etc.).
Siddung	Sit down.
Sinting	Something. Anything useful.
Slampata	Slippers. Shoes made from leather or rubber.
Smaddy	Somebody. Meaning anyone without calling a name.
Smalls	Coins. Small change (for a favour, job, work or other deed).
Soso	Food without meat (Spanish word).
Souja	Soldier.
Soup	Stew with more liquid than vegetables.
Spane	Spain. Columbus discovered Jamaica in 1494.
Spar	A friend, acquaintance.
Spliff	Self-made cigarette (e.g. cannabis).
Strap	Belt made from leather.
Sums	Arithmetic.
Sussoo-sussoo	Whisper. Gossip quietly.
Sweet mouth	Flirt. Philanderer.
Swims	Shrimps. Seafood. Prawns.
Switch	A whip made from bark or fibre.

T

Tallawah	Strongman. Mouthy small woman.
Tan deh	Stay there.
Tan tuddy	Stay still.
Tan up	Stand up.
Tan yah	Stay here.
Tapanarie	Someone posh, sophisticated.
Tea-pot	*See Teele.*
Teck	Take. To receive or steal something.
Teele	Small boy's penis (i.e. toddler's).
Tegreg	Argumentative old woman.
Thredbag	Cloth purse with drawstring worn on body.
Tie-a-leaf	Food cooked and served in a banana leaf (e.g. when out camping).

Tomatis	Tomato plant (old word).
Toona	Cactus plant or its fruit.
Toto	Dark semi-sponge cake cut in squares.
Trace (v.)	To argue repetitively (two people).
Trampoose (v.)	To go from place to place.
Tu	To. I am going to.
Tuh	Too. You are (plural).
Tumato	Tomato fruit.
Tuntid	Not fully grown, immature (e.g. fruit), or to faint (i.e. become confused).
Two-two's	Quickly, pronto. Immediately.

U

Ugli	Not pleasing to the eye (person or thing).
Unckle	Uncle (male relative).
Unoo	All of you. Everyone.
Up	Suffix meaning something bad has happened (e.g. fed up).
Uppity	To think highly of oneself. Pompous.

V

Vial	Small bottle or phial containing liquid.
Vice	Voice.
Voodoo	Witchcraft.

W

Waan	To want or do something.
Wah?	What?
Wan	One.
Wash belly	The last child or sibling a women gave birth to.
Wata	Water.
Watchi watchi	Nosey, like a peeping Tom.
Wax	To eat quickly. Greedy.
Weh?	Where?
White liver	Nymphomaniac. Highly sexed woman.
Wi	We.
Wicked	Nasty, brutal.
Wickid	Good, lovely, great (slang).
Wid	With.
Wi haffi	We have to.
Witch doctor	Obeah man. One who purports to cast spells.

Wouda/Couda	Would/could.
Wrangling	Argument.
Wud	Word.
Wutliss	Worthless (e.g. patois vocabulary, *yuh tuh wutliss*).

X

Xplain	To explain. Simplify.
Xtra	To show off. Extrovert person.

Y

Yagga-yagga	Male youth behaving badly.
Yah	Here.
Yah so	Right here.
Yail	Hail, as in ice. Snow.
Yam	Root vegetable, staple food.
Yampie	Soft, smallish yam.
Yardie	Jamaican living abroad.
Yaws	Chronic sore on foot or leg. Infected sore.
Yes	Yes.
Y'eye	Eye.
Youth	Young man or boy.
Yow	Greeting: Hello.
Yuh	You. (*Mi ah talk tu yuh.*)

Z

Zed	Last letter of the alphabet.
Zephyr	Type of cigarette no longer produced.
Zion	Relating to heaven. Christians of Zionist faith.

THE AUTHOR

Deeta S. Johnson lives in Bristol, but she was born and educated in Jamaica in the 1950s, at a state school and a high school. She emigrated to England in her teens, undertook further education and married a few years later. She qualified as a nurse in the 1970s and studied as an Open University BA undergraduate in the 1980s. She worked full-time as a qualified RMN, SRN, later acquiring diplomas in philosophy (MPhil), stress consultancy (MASC), astrology and reflexology.

Deeta has been passionate about reading and writing since childhood and as an adult she has become interested in journalism and learning languages, reading books on French, Italian, and Swahili and undertaking extensive tuition in Spanish.

She has also contributed several songs to music albums in the USA, and poems to several anthologies, including *Celebration of Poets* in the USA.

She lived in a large Jamaican community in

Birmingham, England, where the Jamaican lingo was used in conversations and songs, and it was there that she completed her research for this *Jamaican Patois Dictionary*.

The author is also a poet and short-story writer and has added some of her works for the reader's relaxation.

DEDICATED TO THE READER

AMBITION

There is a pernicious pride called ambition
Here is one of man's earthly vice.
Ambition is a word full of gumption
Secretly tied with troubles and strife.

The slaves of ambition are bright,
They will keep on flying and plying.
They forget era, age and denying,
They must remember to keep on prying.

Ambitious fighters they defy to keep their aim.
They fight and stake their claim.
To attain their ambition and merit,
There is no sighing, they just keep on trying.

Ancient heroes with comely faces held on to their faith.
They gained their ambition filled with honour and grace.
The beauty of Homer's ambition is still embraced
And erudite Virgil is worshipped in his grave.

Neoclassical heroes, young and old, behold
And the idols of life will slowly unfold,
Achievement and praise will heighten your days.
For material goals are useful to animate souls!

LEISURE WALK

SUMMARY

Barbara Minty was halfway through her ten-mile leisure walk with some friends when she met Pete, who showed concern for her slowness. The route was very rural and Barbara was lagging behind. Pete waited for her and struck up a conversation as they walked.

They told each other about their families, jobs and hobbies, but Pete hinted he had problems. Barbara used her ingenuity to get him talking, and he told her he suffered from dyslexia and had failed his first-year teacher's examination. This was his reason for leaving college to seek help and advice.

Barbara was a shorthand typist, and she felt her English was good enough to help Pete. Not only that, she had fallen in love with him and wanted to get closer to him. She didn't tell him about her feelings, but offered to help with his spellings.

Pete was delighted and was feeling the same about her, so he offered to take her to lunch to discuss the matter.

Barbara thought spellings and the correct pronunciation of words were important. She said yes to his offer.

LEISURE WALK

Sitting on a conveniently shaped rock by the wayside with my right leg raised a few inches off the ground, I proceeded to bandage my sore heel. I leaned my head to the left and looked to the right after hearing the sound of approaching feet.

"Hi, Jenny," I said.

"Hello there," replied Jenny.

"So you finally caught up with us," I said, tying my bootlace.

"Only just," said Jenny. "I didn't think I would get this far with my sore feet."

"And I should be patting myself on the back for walking so many miles," replied my friend Annabel, who was sitting nearby gasping for breath.

The sound of laughter followed this breathless talk.

Despite our tired feet we stood to attention, ready to head off again before we were caught up.

"Hi, girls," said one of the boys in the party.

"Hi, fellows," Jenny and I blurted out together.

"How is it going?" I said, trying to be polite.

"Not too good for the lungs, I gather," said one of the boys. "Only another four miles to go, believe it or not! You girls have just walked six miles," he said.

Feeling and looking more cheerful, I hope, I smiled at everyone and said, "Why don't we all introduce ourselves and stop saying 'girls' and 'fellows'? My name is Barbara Minty and this is my friend Annabel Crutchley."

"And I'm Jenny Jones," said Jenny with a sideways glance at me.

"Hi. I'm called Pete and this is Martin. We work together. And this is Janine and Madeline – who, I believe, is too tired to speak," he added with a sarcastic smile.

"Stop boasting," said Janine. "We'll get to the finishing point before you yet."

Pete gave another broad smile and bowed before both girls, saying, "I beg your humble apologies, ma'am, so please don't finish before my mate and me."

Admiring his sense of humour, I felt like bursting out laughing. But I restrained myself for fear of the others wondering what was so funny.

We proceeded to walk the remaining four

miles, and as our energy began to wane we found ourselves lagging behind in pairs or small groups. I was always a slow walker – a child could walk faster than I could. Pete was very patient, though, and kept looking over his shoulder to urge me on. Everyone was walking almost in single file a half a mile or so later, and I found myself at the back.

I caught up with Pete when he sat down by the side of the road.

"Something wrong?" I said.

"No, just planning to surprise them by zooming past them five minutes before we get to the finishing spot. I'm a very good walker, you see."

"Don't forget your bet with Madeline and Janine," I said. "Remember you and your mate have to beat the girls to it."

"Oh yes," he said, rather apathetically. He picked himself up from the side of the road and walked over to my right side. He looked at me with a gentle smile and said, "Seriously, Barbara, I didn't think it was right to leave a young lady on her own walking down such a rural road. That's why I waited for you."

"You're being very kind and protective," I said.

He smiled and replied, "Kind, possibly, but protective I'm not too sure about."

"Walking on my right, on the outside, is a kind of protection," I said.

"Oh that!" He laughed. "Well, that's only my feeble try at being a gentleman, and you have to thank my mother's upbringing for that."

As we walked I took in the passing scenery. I watched the cows grazing lazily in the fields and the farmers hard at work, and we made way for the odd vehicle that passed us. It was a warm, dry day in July – just right for such activities.

The walk was becoming easier with Pete's talking and his enigmatic smile.

"Tell me about yourself," I said, rather boldly. "That is, if you care to."

"My name is Ravioli," said Pete, changing his accent to Italian. "Now go and look up our family tree."

"Are you always this funny or are you just trying to cheer me up?" I said.

"I thrive on being funny," said Pete, sounding rather serious. "It stops me worrying about my problems."

"What problems?" I asked. "I do hope they are minor ones."

"Well," he said slowly, sounding a little reluctant to talk, "both my parents are in the medical profession: my father is a hospital doctor and my mother an anaesthetist. I suppose that's how they met. I have two sisters and one brother. I am twenty years old and the youngest of the family. I'm trying to become a teacher, but with some difficulty."

"And what is so difficult about that, might I ask?"

"Well, after gaining three A-level passes at school in history, maths and a very low-grade pass in English, I decided I wanted to be a teacher. I've done my first year at teacher training college, but failed my first-year examination."

"Don't they give you a second chance at it?" I asked.

"They certainly do, but the examiner thinks I have got dyslexia, which isn't good for my job."

"I have heard of it vaguely, but I've never met anyone with it before; I don't think I would recognise it anyway," I said.

"You would recognise it if you saw my writing," said Pete with a rather half-hearted grin. "The trouble is that I write words the same way as I pronounce them, leaving out the valuable vowels, just like I did as a child. No wonder I got a low grade in English."

"There must be ways of improving your spelling," I said, trying to sound encouraging.

"Well, the head of the school has suggested that I could stop training for a year and find a temporary teaching job for that period that doesn't involve too much writing; at the same time I've got to get some private tuition in spelling."

"So that's how you come to be working in this area."

"That's right – as a maths teacher. But I also need to see a specialist."

I listened eagerly to his conversation, noting some of his physical traits as he spoke, like the way his lips curled when he laughed and the gleam in his eyes when he smiled. His wavy blonde hair blew gently in the breeze and his arms swayed alongside his strong athletic figure as he walked.

"Let's call in for a cool drink," I said, noticing a refreshment kiosk parked in a lay-by.

Feeling refreshed and more energetic after our long, cold drink, we stepped up our pace for the last two miles of the journey. Pete looked at me – or, rather, down at me; his broad, square shoulders towered at least six inches above mine.

"I suppose I talk too much about myself. I didn't give you much of a chance to say anything," said Pete.

"There isn't much to tell really," I said, "but if you'd like to know more, it goes like this. I came to live and work in the village where the walk started."

"What do you work at?" he asked.

"As a private secretary in the Park Hotel in the square. Home is in the big city I moved from. I like it in the country because it's a lot quieter and more in keeping with my personality and my hobbies."

"What are your hobbies?" asked Pete, growing more inquisitive.

"Walking, writing, birdwatching and I love to look at the trees. I'm fascinated by all kinds of trees. They grow so much bigger in the countryside."

"I know," said Pete. "They keep chopping them down in the big cities. I never told you about my brother, did I? He is a doctor, like my father, and lectures at a well-known university. Both my sisters are training to be teachers and they managed to pass their exams with no trouble at all, which makes me the odd one out.

"Stop feeling sorry for yourself, Pete. You'll pass with flying colours."

"That I may," said Pete, "but when?"

"I'd say a year behind your sisters. After that, with promotion, you could get further than you think."

"I suppose I could," he said, smiling and looking more cheerful.

Suddenly I felt I wanted to see him again, to learn more about his personality and his interests, but most of all to help him with his writing. I saw a small group ahead of us.

"Is that your mate up ahead?"

"It is," said Pete, waving to Martin, who managed a quick look back at us. "I think I can also see Jenny and Annabel just in front of Martin."

Wondering what to say next – how to let him know I cared – I suddenly said, "And how does your fiancée help with your problem?"

"Oh, I'm not engaged," he said. "I did have a girlfriend once, but when I moved here she decided to end the relationship. You see, we were both at college together."

"Honestly," I said, "I feel I would like to help with your problem. One has to be good at English in my job, with all that shorthand and typing to cope with. Perhaps I could help, unless you have someone special you'd rather spend your time with."

"Could you really come and help me?" said Pete. "No, there isn't anyone special at the moment. I like your company, Barbara. I look forward to you coming."

I looked at him smiling for the first time. I felt relaxed with him and more confident.

I continued talking: "Having just moved here myself, I am short of friends and have little or nothing to do in the evenings."

Pete looked at me with that melting smile and brushed a few strands of hair off his forehead.

"I'll ring you at the Park Hotel just before lunch next Monday," he said. "Perhaps we could have lunch together and continue our talk."

Nearing the party ahead of us, I smiled at him and answered, "I look forward to that very much."

We then parted and mingled with the rest of the group to exchange our views at the finishing line.

THE ENLIGHTENMENT

SUMMARY

Martha Faraday was the proud owner of a little bakery her husband, Jake, had left her. She served her village well, but longed for a life of ease and pleasure. Her wish was granted when her only daughter, Connie, a model, invited her to travel on an assignment to Africa. On the aeroplane Martha had the misfortune of sitting on her own, away from Connie and her work party. She was lucky to sit next to a fine man, who spoke to her.

The holiday in Africa was very trying. Martha not only had to carry their luggage over rough terrain, but had to wash their clothes and cook as well.

In the village, shopping for food, they came across a young boy who told them about a location some miles away where filming was going on. Shortly afterwards they were heading for Rhino Creek, the location. Miles, the lead photographer, was hoping to show off his extrovert personality.

Martha struck lucky, standing in for one of the supporting actresses, who fell ill with malaria. Her near resemblance and similarity in age made Martha ideal for the part. The uncanny thing was that the fine man she met on the plane was there too. Miles and his assistant got in on the act, helping the cameramen, and Connie and Debbie got parts as extras, but the fun didn't end there. Connie was jealous of her mother's leading role and Martha had a job making it up to her.

THE ENLIGHTENMENT

Martha Faraday, a widow, had two grown-up children who chose careers she neither knew nor cared about.

She made her livelihood from the little bakery her husband, Jake, had left her, without any help from Pete or Connie.

Connie was always going off to wild locations to do her modelling. This worried Martha because Connie was once mauled by a wildcat in the African jungle, pecked by a vicious bird in the Caribbean and carried away by an angry elephant she was riding in the Himalayas. As for Pete, Martha lost count of the many black eyes and bruises he collected during his boxing career.

Everyone close to her warned her about becoming a nervous wreck if she did not pay less attention to the bakery and get out more. In such a small village as theirs Martha could not envisage herself adopting a new, more exciting lifestyle, even though she was only forty-four. But when Connie invited her on a holiday trip to watch her model, little did she know that the journey was to change the humdrum routine she was used to into a life of glamour and excitement which would make even her daughter jealous.

"Are you sure you want me to chaperone you to Africa?" she asked, thinking she had misheard.

"Certainly," Connie replied without hesitation. "Africa can be a pretty scary place at times still, you know."

"How scary do you mean?" asked an anxious-looking Martha. "You don't mean there are wild animals walking around the tents at night, do you?"

Connie scratched her head and continued to sort out her wardrobe. "Not exactly, Mother, but pretty close to it. It's possible they will have animals in cages or on leads to complement the setting."

Martha looked at her worriedly. "I'm not sure I want to be in the company of wild animals, Connie, cages or no cages; at the same time I suppose I'd better be brave and go with the saying 'I'll try anything once'."

"That's the spirit," Connie replied, smiling. "We leave in a month's time, so have your wardrobe, your passport and your traveller's cheques ready by then; and by the way, Barney Miller has decided to pay half your return fare."

"That's very nice of him, but who is Barney Miller?"

"Oh, he's the boss of the agency that employs me. Since you're acting as chaperone, they figured they owe you a discount."

Martha looked at her, wide-eyed with curiosity.

"I hope there are no chores involved. I'm going for a rest. Slaving over a hot oven all these years deserves a nice rest."

Connie gave her a quick look and a wry smile.

"You'll get plenty of rest, but I dare say if you're standing around doing nothing you'll be asked to serve beverages or hold an umbrella. That sort of thing will earn you some compliments. The natives love it."

"I can see what sort of holiday I'm going to have with you to look after," Martha replied, laughing.

A month later five of them piled out of a hired wagon at the airport to board the plane. There was the chief photographer, Miles; his assistant, Roland; Debbie, a second model; and Connie. As they struggled through the airport barriers with their hand luggage Martha could see a whole new world opening up in front of her. Until then she had never realised that so many people travelled the earth. People were going north, east, west and south for hundreds of different reasons.

As she watched a variety of humans helter-skeltering about, she stumbled over someone's suitcase before suddenly realising that her party was way ahead of her, going towards the runway.

Connie stepped out of line, waited for her and gave her an impatient look.

"Try and stick with the group, Mother, or we may lose each other."

Martha, fighting her way through the crowd, told her, "Never mind me – you go ahead and sit with your friends. I'll be on the plane."

Connie gave a bemused smile. "You won't be able to sit where you like, Mother; furthermore, our tickets are probably all consecutive."

Connie was wrong about the tickets. Martha had bought hers separately, and she had to sit elsewhere. This pleased Martha because she did not feel obliged to chat to the stranger sitting next to her; she therefore had plenty of time to muse.

As she sat looking out of the window at the white clouds and endless expanse of ocean beneath her, she thought about the little bakery she had left behind. It was not shut – she had left her cousin Walter to run it. She had felt sorry for Walter ever since he became almost paralysed and unfit for work. Having an emotionally weak-willed wife like Phyllis, and a young son at boarding school, did not help his position either.

'Yes,' she thought, 'Walter will certainly amuse himself while I'm away.'

Several hostesses walked around, serving cocktails. Martha relaxed in her seat, sipped her rum 'bamboozle' and listened to the ebbing sound of drums and maracas in the background. Mesmerised by the whole affair, she dozed off, thinking she could not take it all in.

In her sleep, she heard a voice speaking to her. Suddenly she woke up and looked out of the window and wondered whether she was over Africa and just about to land. Realising it was the man sitting next to her who spoke, she smiled at him.

He smiled at her, and spoke again: "I'm sorry I woke you up, ma'am. I didn't realise you were sleeping."

"That's quite all right," Martha told him with an embarrassed look on her face. "I must have dozed off."

The stranger looked at her again.

"My name is Jack Delaney. The scenery out there is so breathtaking, I couldn't help but want to share it with you. Just look at those grey and blue skies chasing each other. And the sun! You can't see it from here, but you know it's there because it glistens on the aeroplane's wing every few seconds."

Martha stared out of the window and nodded in agreement. Softly she told him, "Yes, it's beautiful, isn't it?" Turning to face him, she said, "I might as well introduce myself. My name is Martha Faraday."

"Might I call you Martha or Mrs Faraday?" asked the stranger.

Martha shrugged her shoulders. "Oh, either will do nicely, but you can call me Martha. Everybody does, including Connie and Pete."

He looked at her, somewhat puzzled. "Connie? Pete?"

Martha smiled at him. "They are the names of my two children. Connie is sitting on this very plane, away up front with her working partners. She's on a modelling assignment."

Jack listened attentively and appeared to be puzzled about her presence in a seat so far from her daughter.

"Your daughter's job sounds very nice, Martha, but why have you got to travel with her?"

Martha considered his inquisitive question. Smiling at him, she told him, "I'm going for a holiday. It was Connie's idea about me chaperoning her while holidaying. I haven't had one since I became a widow eight years ago. Jake made sure

I kept my livelihood going in the little bakery he owned. He taught me everything about dough making." She threw her head back, stared at the roof of the plane and expressed how she felt about her little business. "It gives me great pleasure at Christmas and Easter to create novelty figures in pastry for the children. You ought to see how their little faces light up." Suddenly she repositioned herself in her seat, stopped talking and apologised to him. "Pardon me for carrying on, Mr Delaney. All this talk about kneading dough and making snowmen must bore you terribly."

He smiled at her amusedly. "Far from it, Martha; in fact, I find it quite interesting. It's a far cry from what I do for a living. That's what makes it so interesting. It's new to the ears. So don't you think I'm bored by it. I tell you, there's nothing worse than talking shop with people in the same business as I am. It sends me off to sleep."

Martha thought he was very funny and laughed at his comments. As she laughed she noted the outline of his face, his tall, lean figure, and his shoulder-length hair swept to one side on his forehead.

'Forty-eight years – that is more or less his age,' thought Martha. 'He is extremely handsome and debonair, despite his greying sideburns. I wonder what his motives for travelling to Africa are.'

As if he read her thoughts, he then told her, "I'm going to Africa on business. The company I work for asked me to go and look at a place – a nice location. I figure I'll be there for several weeks." He laughed, making it known he was not sorry either.

"Good for you!" replied a disenchanted Martha. "It sounds like an interesting place. I hope you find it."

Still looking pleased with himself, he replied, "It had better be just the type of place we're after or I won't have a job. The others will be following in a week's time."

Suddenly the announcement came for them to fasten their seat belts for landing. Everyone got excited, peering out of windows over one another's heads and shoulders for a glimpse of Africa. No one was interested in conversation at that time, only a safe landing into glorious sunshine.

As they left the plane Jack Delaney gave Martha the option to go first.

"You have a wonderful holiday now," he told her, waving. "No doubt we shall see each other on safari."

Martha smiled and waved, but said nothing. Meeting Jack Delaney was a good start to her holiday, but she was sorry their acquaintance had to end so soon.

Arriving at the hotel, she unpacked everything. Connie and her friend Debbie obliged by keeping out of the way. They manicured each other's fingernails and experimented with their hair. Martha thought she would give them the day off, rather than shout at them. Connie walked into the room a few minutes later.

"Have you by any chance unpacked my yellow shorts?" she asked. "I'm going to have a shower, and then I'll change into something comfortable. The sunshine is too glorious to ignore."

Martha look at her alarmingly.

"Sunbathing so soon? Well, what about Miles and Roland? Won't they be joining us?"

"Yes, certainly. They'll be joining us soon, but not for work – for tea and supper, but not work. Miles never works on the day he lands, even if it's early morning. He says he likes to get the feel of the place first, watch the natives, see the animals, hear the local music. All these factors make him a better director behind the camera.

Martha sat mesmerised listening to Connie's description of Miles. Suddenly, as if in a trance, she got out of her seat and began walking round the room.

She whispered, "Yes, I can see what you mean. I can actually feel it myself." Gradually her pace got quicker, and with hands thrusting about she chanted, "Throw your head about like the natives, Connie. Yank your hips to the right like they do, Connie. Stroke your fingers through your hair, Connie. Let it stream backwards carelessly with the wind, Connie. And don't forget to smile, Connie – show your teeth while doing all that."

The sound of Debbie's footsteps approaching the room made her stop.

"Hey, Mother," shouted Connie, "I didn't know you could act. That was brilliant."

Martha replied cheerfully, "That was no acting; that was mimicry. In other words I was just trying to get into the holiday spirit. I hope Miles Daley doesn't hear of it."

Connie smiled lovingly at her. "I can see you intend to make the most of your three weeks in Africa. What about that nice man you were sitting with on the plane – the one you introduced to me when I passed to go to the powder room? Is he holidaying in these parts?

"Oh, you mean Mr Delaney. He was travelling alone but obviously married. I told him all about you, Pete, Jake and the bakery, but he said nothing about his social background. He told me he was here on business, looking over a place."

"What place?" Connie asked.

"I don't know. I think he was about to tell me when the plane landed. So did my thoughts, only mine was a crash-landing. I probably did crash-land. Why else would his leaving worry me? The only thing he said when we parted was he hoped we would meet on safari, which is a million-to-one chance in a place like Africa."

Miles Daley was all set for work next day. He was up at 5 a.m. and made sure the hotel staff woke the others up in time for 6 a.m. breakfast.

"Breakfast 6 a.m.," screamed Martha. "I can't take it – I'll be sick."

"No, you won't," shouted Miles. "In this part of the world everything starts at 5 a.m., so by 6 a.m. you'll be starving. The heat takes a lot of your energy away, even when you're asleep! At 6 a.m. there'll be so much noise and commotion going on outside you won't be able to sleep anyway."

Every morning they sauntered down to the breakfast room with their luggage for the day's shooting: refreshments, water and fresh clothing. Everyone seemed well alert and rather used to that type of life, except Martha.

Miles took turns with Roland to drive the Jeep over the rugged roads. Debbie and Connie posed for titillating pictures under waterfalls. Among sauntering giraffes, leaping antelopes and beautiful flamingos. It was obvious Connie and Debbie were enjoying every minute of their work, not forgetting Miles and Roland. They got their satisfaction by turning out good shots, but at the moment it was Martha and the photographers who were doing all the hard work. Martha carried the girls' suitcases, looked after their clothes, helped with their make-up and prepared the refreshments. Roland and Miles had to move from one beauty spot to another with heavy equipment on their backs, around their necks and under their arms.

Miles was in a good mood the first week. Apart from taking snaps, he went shopping with Martha and the girls for food. The only odd thing was that he always took a camera.

As they strolled through the native market one day a little boy of about ten approached him, shouting, "You film man, bwana? You from ol' Rhino Creek? Me very good helper if you take me with you."

Miles picked up a peculiar-looking fruit and weighed it in his hand. He looked menacingly at the boy.

"Me no from Rhino Creek, boy. Me no film man. Now shove off!"

The boy stood there, looking disappointed, with his head down.

The fruit seller butted in: "Boy is right, bwana. They're making film over at ol' Rhino Creek. Very good film. Everybody go there looking for work."

Miles looked at him sheepishly. "How do you know?" he asked the fruit seller.

"Because they come twice a week in two Jeeps to buy plenty food and fruits. Sometimes they bring big camera on sticks and film whole market, and anybody they film they give money."

Miles patted the boy on the head. "You know, er—"

"The name is Obisotho."

"Well, Obisotho, I'm not a film man, but perhaps you would like a little job taking some fruit back to our hotel?"

Obisotho's eyes lit up with glee.

"Yes, bwana. This one very nice fruit. This one also, and that one very popular. People from film buy plenty of those."

The fruit seller confirmed Obisotho's statement and prepared a basket of fruit to Miles's approval.

Roland was less of an extrovert. He never spoke unless someone else spoke first. In the village square the only things he was interested in were the ornaments and other artefacts the natives made. He bought pieces of all shapes and sizes to take home. Apart from that he was well capable of helping and advising when Miles got stuck.

In the bar that night Miles enquired about Rhino Creek.

The barman replied, "Ol' Rhino Creek? It's about twenty miles from here, sir. Everywhere you look it's breathtaking scenery. There is a mountain peak on one side, a waterfall on the other, a camp near the centre. It's a park, with all kinds of animals, rivers, streams, beautiful gardens, beautiful trees . . . You name it, it's there, sir."

"Sounds very grand," Miles said to him cheerfully. "I hear they are making a film there."

The barman nodded.

"Our work here is almost finished. Perhaps we'll take a ride over there tomorrow and have a look at them working."

The barman smiled and poured himself another drink.

"You can even finish taking pictures of models there," he said. "Very good pictures you'll get. Famous part of Africa."

Next day, as they trundled along twenty miles of rough road, through jungle thicket, passing hungry wild animals, Martha got worried.

She fumed at Miles Daley: "I suppose you're enjoying all this? It was your idea for us to stray so far away from our base. Well! I'd rather be back in civilisation. The sooner we leave for England the better."

Connie was getting worried about her mother's temper.

Worriedly she told her, "Be brave and keep quiet. The wild animals won't get to us. All we're doing is changing our venue for a day to make our trip more interesting."

Miles could not help laughing. He giggled and chuckled at their conversation without commenting before adding, "I'm having a wonderful time. What about you, Roland?"

Sitting diagonally from Debbie, Roland was interested in her smile.

The film crew were pleased to see a party of English folks approaching and welcomed them in. Miles introduced himself as lead photographer looking for a hot location.

"Well, you've come to the right place," the man replied in a broad Texan accent. "I'm the producer. My man Frank found us this beautiful place. Them folks back in Texas are gonna love this picture show."

Debbie whispered to Connie, "They are Americans, Connie. Now is our chance to show off our looks."

Martha overheard her. "Well, Connie, you might just be disappointed. I spoke to two on my way in and they weren't Americans. In fact, I recognised their accent and it was common Cockney."

Connie, being her usual confident self, replied,

"Never mind the accent, Debbie. Mingling with the film set is what we want."

Although life was buzzing at Rhino Creek, something seemed wrong. People were moving about, putting up props, taking down props and standing about talking in groups, but the cameras were not rolling.

Martha and the girls wandered around, looking at everything. Miles strolled around, trying to look important with an oversized camera round his neck.

"What's the name of the film?" Miles asked a friendly-looking face. "If it ain't *The African Queen*, Bob's my uncle."

The man looked at him sideways and grinned.

"I'm afraid Bob's your uncle, because it ain't. It's called *The Lion Tamer*."

Miles returned his grin and remarked, "That's very appropriate, but why aren't the cameras rolling? Where is the star? Has he or she forgotten the lines?"

The man replied, "One of the supporting actresses has fallen ill. We can't work without her."

"We? Her?" asked Miles, "Yes, me – I'm the director. She is supposed to be the star's mother-in-law. There are only four actresses on the set. The other three are very young. The make-up artist says he hasn't got the material to make a twenty-year-old girl look fifty – not here in the jungle in this heat. Her face would crack. I tell you she'll have to crawl on that set tomorrow. I shan't wait another day."

Miles stood up with elbows raised at his side. He looked as if he was part of the team.

"Aren't you being a little hard on the poor woman?" he asked the director. "She's probably caught a fever."

The director raised his eyebrows in anger, but before he could speak the producer, Jack, walked towards them smiling. He patted the director on the shoulder.

"Richard Warburton, I've got some good news and some bad news for you."

Richard gave him a strained look.

"Well, let me have the bad news first."

"The bad news is Mrs Hamburg was seen by the Doctor and he's ordered her to go into hospital. He says her malaria is very bad."

Richard stared at him in disbelief.

"Well, if that's the bad news, Jack, there can't be any good news. This picture is finished. Do you think I can afford to pay a whole cast and feed ten hungry lions until Mrs Hamburg leaves hospital?"

Jack Delaney backed away from him in fear.

"Well, I'm very optimistic that the good news

might help. The rumour is that there is almost a lookalike of Mrs Hamburg walking round the film set this very minute. Perhaps she could stand in for her.

"Have you seen her?" Richard asked quietly.

"No. They tell me she came in with the small party to look around."

Richard threw his hands up in the air and said, "Well, find her. Bring her to me now, before she leaves."

Just then Miles Daley butted in: "Just a minute. I came in with two young models and the mother of one of the girls. You don't mean Martha Faraday, do you? She's about forty-four, but she's no actress. The only acting she's capable of is acting the fool. She gave me a right ticking off on the way here for driving through jungles and scaring her with wildcats.

Richard nodded his head and smiled optimistically. "That's the kind of star I like – one with a bit of punch. I hope she's a good lookalike."

Jack Delaney, looking more confident, told him, "I never realised it was Martha Faraday they were talking about. We sat next to each other on the plane from London. She was staying in a village some thirty miles from here."

Jack and Miles found Martha and the girls wandering around talking to film cameramen. Jack shouted her name. Martha turned round.

"Well, if it isn't Jack. Small Africa, isn't it? Is this the place you came to look over, then?"

Jack replied, "Um, yes. They're making an American picture for worldwide distribution."

"But, Jack, you're British."

"I know I am, but this film is for international distribution and you're to star in it."

Martha held on to her bag and felt her chest to see if she was still breathing.

"First you woke me up on the plane, and now you're playing childish games with me."

Miles Daley interrupted: "It's no game, Martha – he means it. One of the characters, your lookalike, was admitted to hospital with malaria, which has left them in a spot."

Suddenly Connie intervened: "My mother knows nothing about acting. I suggest you use your understudy. Bringing my mother on this holiday has been a bad enough experience for her."

Richard Warburton, growing impatient, had tracked the others down. Scanning Martha from afar, he decided she was right for the part. "Your mother not an actress?" he asked Connie. "Why don't you let her decided for herself? In some scenes she'll appear in the background; scenes with dialogue will take up only about thirty minutes, and that's including the other people's lines. I'm sure she can manage to learn her part by morning."

Martha nodded her head in approval and smiled surreptitiously, beaming with pride.

Connie was adamant and persistent with her protest: "But we have to get back to town before dark," she said. "It's all right for Mother, but what about me? I can't afford to get my skin blemished. There're too many mosquitoes out here. No wonder your lady has got malaria."

"Me too," added Debbie. "My skin has to be flawless."

"Don't worry about going back tonight," Miles reassured them. "Tomorrow at sunset will do nicely. In fact, I want to take some pictures of the girls in that lovely park near here, and I intend to pick up a few tips from the cameramen here. Who knows, I might even switch jobs when I get back to England."

Roland, who stood quietly taking it all in, laughed at Miles's comment, and taunted him, "When would you like me to start calling you Sir Miles?"

Martha got impatient and shouted at them: "You're all being very childish. Well, I'm staying. This is an opportunity I won't let slip. You can all return without me if you like. I'll make my own way back to England whenever."

With that, Richard Warburton giggled and ushered her along. "That's what I was waiting to hear, Mrs Faraday – your decision. Now go with Jack Delaney and sign the necessary papers. After that he'll take you to the make-up artist to prepare you for a screen test. When I've seen the screen test, I'll give you the script with your lines for you to learn tonight. Oh, and Jack Delaney will see that you all get looked after free of charge tonight."

With that, he walked away and left them to their fate.

Within two hours Martha had undergone a quick transformation. The hairdressers and make-up artists had made a star of her.

It was very hard, if not totally impossible, to distinguish between her and the shots of Mrs Hamburgh in earlier scenes. Her silky, dark hair, her height and her figure – everything was perfect. Even the tone of her voice was exactly right.

Martha was loving every minute of her star treatment and acted the part well. The character she played was a sophisticated, fastidious mother-in-law who interfered in everything her daughter and son-in-law did.

Her son-in-law, the lion tamer, got his own back by using the lions to frighten her so he and his wife could have some privacy. Martha immersed herself in the part. Her character had a crisp walk, a posh accent and a nose for picking up hints, not forgetting a tongue to make people cry.

The only thing that worried her was that she could see Connie was jealous. Connie was the one with the youthful looks, the gorgeous figure, the beautiful mermaid-like hair. Why didn't she get a part? Martha asked herself. Still, Connie was her own beloved daughter. They must never quarrel.

Placing Connie on her knee an hour before filming was due to start, she told her, "Don't be hard on me getting this part, Connie. It just happens that they want an older person. You've brought me on a holiday of a lifetime, and a holiday of a lifetime it has been. That I'm grateful for. You're still young and beautiful and I'm sure someday you'll accomplish your dream of a lifetime."

Connie hugged her mother and kissed her on the forehead. "I apologise for not encouraging you, Mother," she said. "As you say, I'm still young with endless opportunities ahead."

No sooner had Connie got off Martha's knee than Jack Delaney came over and told Connie Richard Warburton had suggested she and Debbie fall into one of the scenes as extras. No signatures were needed for their parts, but he suggested they leave their names and addresses for future reference. Connie could not believe her ears.

Martha winked at Connie and whispered, "See what I told you?"

Miles and Roland had their dream of a lifetime helping with the film cameras and had their names entered in the credits.

As they collected their payment and drove out of Rhino Creek, they were stopped by a small boy begging a lift. Miles braked sharply and reversed back in a hurry.

Peering at the boy, he shouted, "My, if it ain't Obisotho!"

There was silence, then a peeping session, then everyone shouted simultaneously, "It is Obisotho!"

"What brought you so far from home? Is there no school today?" Miles asked.

The boy gave him a manly reply: "Obisotho come here to look for work. Obisotho oldest of seven children. Obisotho work some days, go school some days. Obisotho need lift from bwana to go home with parcel."

"Jump in," Miles told him with a broad grin on his face. "Sit next to anyone you fancy."

"Sweet child," Martha declared, peering down at him.

"He can sit next to me any time."

"And did you find work, Obisotho?" Miles giggled.

"No, bwana. Work no find, but film people give me clothes, shoes, money and food. All sorts to take home for everyone in family. Bwana say he was no film man back at market the day Obisotho take fruit basket to hotel, but Bwana did come to ol' Rhino Creek. Very funny."

"We came looking for work too, Obisotho, and we came to see film man make picture. That's why we came to ol' Rhino Creek."

The boy gave an angelic grin, nodded his head as the Jeep rocked from side to side and replied, "Bwana, like Obisotho, no luck with work."

With that he shut up for the remaining journey except for pointing out strange animals and saying thanks when Miles dropped him off.

Three days later, as they boarded the plane for home, Martha looked back at Africa and said to Connie, "Pete and Walter will need a lot of convincing when we tell them all that has happened."